Piano
Grade 4

Pieces & Exercises
for Trinity College London exams

2015-2017

Published by
Trinity College London
www.trinitycollege.com

Registered in the UK
Company no. 02683033
Charity no. 1014792

Printed in Great Britain by Caligraving Ltd.

Presto

Third movement from Sonata in A, Hob. XVI/26

Josef Haydn
(1732-1809)

Soldiers' Chorus

from *Faust*

Arr. Janet and Alan Bullard

Charles Gounod
(1818-1893)

Alla marcia ♩. = 100

5

Allegro moderato

First movement from Sonatine, op. 300

Ed. Peter Wild

Louis Köhler
(1820-1886)

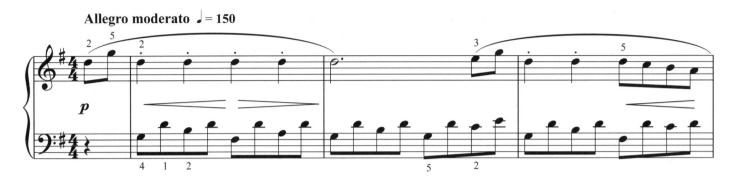

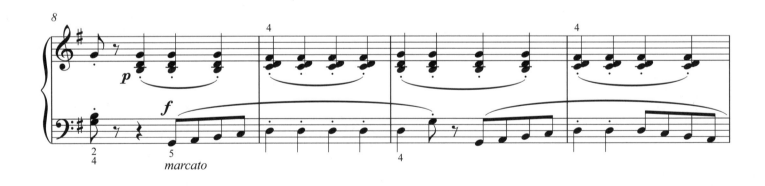

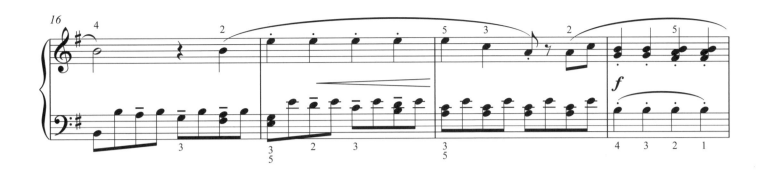

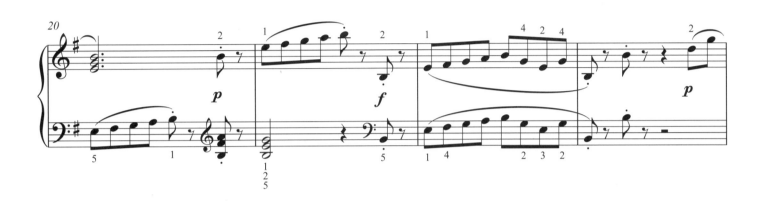

Der Schmetterling und die Blume

'June' from *The Seasons*

Nicolai Podgornov
(born 1950)

[Blank page to facilitate page turns]

Sonatina no.16

in G minor

Georg Anton Benda
(1722-1795)

Forty Winks

Mark Tanner
(born 1963)

Garden Path

Elissa Milne
(born 1967)

Matsuri

(Japanese Festival)

Michael McMillan
(born 1980)

Cucumber Jam

Ben Crosland
(born 1968)

Exercises

1a. Cycling Holiday – tone, balance and voicing

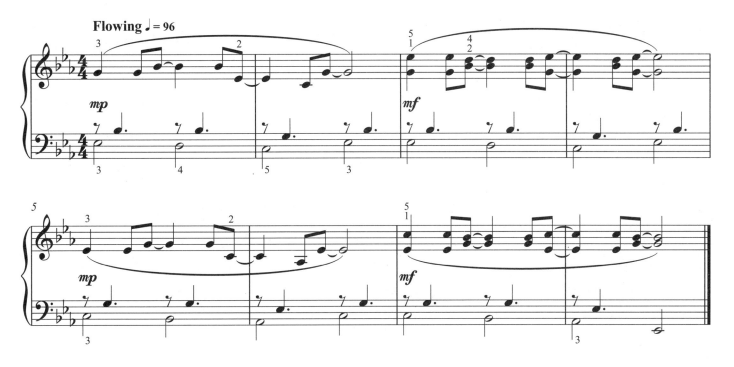

1b. Major to Minor – tone, balance and voicing

2a. Arches – co-ordination

2b. Opposite Views – co-ordination

3a. Cheeky Charlie – finger & wrist strength and flexibility

3b. Rolling Wrist – finger & wrist strength and flexibility